English Activity Book

for ages 9-10

This CGP book is bursting with fun activities to build up children's skills and confidence.

It's ideal for extra practice to reinforce what they're learning in primary school. Enjoy!

Published by CGP

Editors:
Keith Blackhall, Alex Fairer, Becca Lakin, Hannah Roscoe and James Summersgill

With thanks to Alison Griffin and Catherine Heygate for the proofreading.

With thanks to Lottie Edwards for the copyright research.

ISBN: 978 1 78908 733 8

Printed by Elanders Ltd, Newcastle upon Tyne.
Clipart on the cover and throughout the book from Corel®
Cover design concept by emc design ltd.

Contents

Word types

Nouns are naming words. Adjectives describe nouns or noun phrases.

The tired baby sleeps soundly in his high chair.

adjective ⟶   ⟵ noun

Verbs are doing or being words. Adverbs can describe verbs, adjectives or other adverbs.

The child plays
happily by herself.

adverb   verb

The book is
really long.

adverb   adjective

The team played very
poorly yesterday.

adverb

Now Try These

1. Underline the verb in each sentence below, then change it to a new verb that still makes sense. Write your new verbs on the dotted lines.

   Bosede and Ian walk to the beach.   ➡   ....

   Marius made a cake for his birthday.   ➡   ....

   I saw an eagle on my way to school.   ➡   ....

   She likes her mother's dresses.   ➡   ....

2. Underline the word that the adverb in bold is describing below. Then, tick the box to show if the word you have underlined is a verb or an adjective.

   Briony sings **sweetly** to her son.   ☐ verb   ☐ adjective

   My dad is **too** competitive at board games.   ☐ verb   ☐ adjective

   It was **unusually** busy at the park today.   ☐ verb   ☐ adjective

   The girl ran **speedily** down the road.   ☐ verb   ☐ adjective

3. Write a suitable word to complete each sentence. Then, draw a line to match each sentence to the word type of the word you've written.

Rasheed .... to the supermarket.

noun

I decided to wear my .... jumper.

adjective

Her cat .... scratches the furniture.

verb

Delilah poured the soup into a ....

adverb

4. Use the noun, adjective and adverb from each box to write a sentence.

swan
elegant
gracefully

....

....

tales
hilarious
always

....

....

thief
shiny
silently

....

....

An Extra Challenge

Shufen has written a story about a magician. Can you add some adjectives and adverbs to Shufen's story to make it more interesting?

Ikenna walked up to the stall where a magician in a robe stood waiting. She smiled and started to shuffle the cards on the table. She fanned the cards out in front of him and he plucked one out. After studying it, he returned it to her. With a tap of her wand, the deck vanished. He looked at her. She winked at him and told him to check underneath his shoe. He lifted his foot to reveal his card.

Do you know your adjectives
from your adverbs? Tick a box.

Degrees of possibility

How It Works

Some adverbs can show you how possible or certain something is.

It will surely rain today.   Maybe I'll bring an umbrella.

It will definitely rain today.   Perhaps I'll bring an umbrella.

'surely' and 'definitely' are more certain than 'maybe' and 'perhaps'.

Modal verbs can also show you how possible or certain something is.

He will visit me.   He might visit me.

He shall visit me.   He should visit me.

'will' and 'shall' are more certain than 'might' and 'should'.

Now Try These

1. Underline the adverb in each sentence below. Then, number the sentences from most certain (1) to least certain (3).

    Helen possibly won't have time to wash the dishes.   ☐

    I will definitely have a slice of that huge chocolate cake.   ☐

    Bill and Ted will probably go to the theme park with me.   ☐

2. Add an adverb to each sentence below to make it less certain.
    Use a different adverb in each sentence.

    Dmitry is .... going to go fishing tomorrow.

    .... I'll order a strawberry milkshake.

    I think that Megan will .... win the race today.

    .... he won't find the hidden message.

3. Circle the modal verb that makes each sentence more certain.

Tristan **will** / **might** have to go to the vets.

My parents **must** / **could** drive me to the library.

Nick **should** / **shall** brush his teeth every day.

Sofia and Emilia **can** / **must** take the dog for a walk.

4. Write a sentence of your own using each of the modal verbs below.
   When you're finished, tick the sentence that shows certainty.

could

☐

....

might

☐

....

will

☐

....

An Extra Challenge

Look at the picture below. Can you write a sentence to describe each person using the prompts on the left? Then see if you can colour the sentences that show certainty blue and the sentences that show possibility red.

Lucy will probably...

Daniel may...

Kieran might...

Sid must...

Marta is certainly...

Could you possibly tick a
box to show how you did?

Relative clauses

How It Works

A relative clause is a type of subordinate clause.
Relative pronouns, such as 'who', 'whose', 'that' and 'which', are often used to introduce relative clauses. 'Where' and 'when' can also introduce relative clauses.

I'm going to visit my uncle (whose) cat is very greedy.

↑ relative pronoun   ↖ relative clause

Sometimes, the relative pronoun can be left out, and the sentence will still make sense.

The toy car (that) I bought last year has already broken.

This sentence would still make sense without the relative pronoun 'that'.   Relative clauses can also appear in the middle of sentences.

Now Try These

1. Draw lines to match each main clause to a relative clause that makes a sensible sentence.

| I can't wait to go back to the café | that were always covered in snow. |

| Gary loved hiking in the mountains | which starts at eight o'clock. |

| My new neighbour is Dr Petrov | who is a famous scientist. |

| Farah needs a dress for the party | where we had the best apple pie. |

2. Rewrite the sentences below without the relative pronouns.

There is the man who I saw looking for his keys earlier.

....

The soup that Rachel was preparing smelt delicious.

....

6

3. Underline the relative clause in each sentence below.
   Then, write the relative pronoun on the dotted lines.

   The scarf that my nan knitted me is very warm. ....

   Max, whose car had broken down, asked me for help. ....

   Are there any lakes nearby which we can swim in? ....

   The hotel that is around the corner has a new chef. 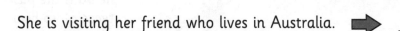 ....

   She is visiting her friend who lives in Australia.  ....

4. Add your own relative clause to each sentence below.

   I am reading the book ....

   The cinema .... is closed today.

   Kara helped the boy ....

   Lesley, ..., was late for school.

An Extra Challenge

Can you write a sentence with a relative clause to describe each of these pictures?

Are your clauses a cause for celebration? Tick a box.

Homophones

How It Works

Homophones are words that sound the same, but have different meanings and spellings.

herd →

A herd is a group of animals, such as cows.

← heard

heard is the past tense of 'to hear'.

Now Try These

1. Tick the sentences below that contain a spelling mistake.
   Write the correct spellings in the box on the right.

   The bride walked gracefully down the isle. ☐

   Alfred pours himself a glass of milk. ☐

   The stormy sky was the colour of steal. ☐

   I think that roses are a cymbal of love. ☐

   Sharks often prey on fish and seals. ☐

2. Circle the right spelling of each word to complete the sentences below.

   Anton wanted the tailor to **altar / alter** his suit.

   Priya raced **passed / past** on her motorbike.

   Kofi was flattered by Robert's **compliment / complement**.

   A cold **draft / draught** crept in through the old door.

   Do you know **who's / whose** going to pick me up later?

3. Complete each sentence below using a pair of homophones from the box.

> guessed / guest   sight / site   knot / not   hire / higher   root / route

I do .... think that you should tie that .... there.

You need to .... a guide to climb .... up.

Janice .... that their .... would be late.

You should take the .... that passes the broken tree ....

The .... of the ancient burial .... was impressive.

4. Write each of these words in a sentence.

peace ➡ ....

piece ➡ ....

current ➡ ....

currant ➡ ....

An Extra Challenge

The boxes on the right give clues for five pairs of homophones. Can you work out the clues and write down each pair of homophones?

Then see if you can write a paragraph that uses at least one word from each pair of homophones.

> The narrow part of your body above your hips

> Not moving

> A period of seven days

> A group of musicians

> Materials you use for writing

> Cause something to split into pieces

> Prevented from doing something by law

> Another word for the noun 'rubbish'

> Lacking strength or energy

> Something you do to slow down a bike or car

How did it go? Did you find meaning in these pages?

Tricky words

Be careful — there are some words that are tricky to spell.

seize

plough though rough

biscuit

Some words don't follow spelling rules. 'seize' doesn't follow the 'i' before 'e' rule.

The letters 'ough' can be used to make lots of different sounds.

Some words contain silent letters that you can't hear when you say the word out loud.

Now Try These

1. Add either 'ie' or 'ei' to the words below to complete the sentences.

There were a var........ty of delicious smells coming from the kitchen.

I saw a huge spider staring at me from the c........ling.

This morning, Felix rec........ved a peculiar parcel in the post.

I think I need to include more prot........n in my diet.

Dorothy greeted the fr........ndly kitten excitedly.

2. Draw lines to match the sentences that contain words with the same 'ough' sound.

Pradeep kneads the pizza **dough**.	The pigs ate noisily from the **trough**.
I've had **enough** of your jokes.	Antonio thinks that he is **tough**.
He **sought** the help of a wizard.	I feel tired even **though** I've slept.
Denise needs some **cough** medicine.	Heidi **fought** with her parents.

3. Circle the correct spelling of each word to complete the sentences below.

The actor **boughed / bowed** after his performance.

He couldn't break **through / threw** the thick ice.

Leanne's dog has a very **ruff / rough** coat.

Her gift to me was very **thoughtful / thortful**.

4. Underline the spelling mistake in each sentence below.
   Write the correct spelling on the dotted lines.

Silvia loves to nit scarves for all her relatives.  ....

Gosts wander the halls of the old mansion.  ....

The students lisened to the teacher attentively. ....

Nathan has taken a rong turn in his car. ....

5. For each misspelt word, write a sentence that uses the correct spelling of the word.

nieghbour	....
brort	....
rasberries	....

An Extra Challenge

Lionel has written in his diary, but he's missed out a silent letter from some of the words. Can you help him rewrite his diary entry to include all the silent letters?

On a rainy autum night, I had to walk half a mile to fix the lighthouse keeper's bath. Looking at the stormy sene outside, I onestly considered not going. Then I felt gilty because I was the only plumer on the iland.

The hilly walk made my musles ache and I was relieved when I finally climed the steps and nocked on the door. The keeper ansered but told me she didn't need my help any more, then closed the door. I brisled at her rudeness but held my tongue. Wile I trudged home, I started to dout my career choice.

How did it go? Did anything on these pages trick you?

Direct speech

How It Works

Direct speech is the words that someone says. Direct speech goes inside inverted commas and always begins with a capital letter.

I exclaimed, "Let's do a jigsaw!"   "Where does this go?" asked Isla.

Put a comma before the speech starts.

You must end direct speech with a punctuation mark inside the inverted commas.

You don't need a capital letter here.

Direct speech can also be broken up into two parts.

"In that gap," Maud replied, "right in front of you."

Put a comma here because the sentence hasn't finished.

You need a comma before the second bit of speech.

You don't need a capital letter if the second bit of speech is part of the same sentence.

Put punctuation here because the sentence has ended.

Now Try These

1. Rewrite the sentences below so that the direct speech comes at the end.

   "Are you there?" asked Zoey. ....

   "Stop that!" shouted Frank. ....

   "There's the pizza," he said. ....

2. Write an answer to each question below using direct speech. Make sure you use the right punctuation.

   "What did you do at the weekend, Veronica?" asked Jayan.

   ....

   "Why are you in trouble, Kwame?" asked Iris.

   ....

3. Rewrite the sentences below so that the direct speech is broken up into two parts.

"Thank you, that is very kind of you," said Joe.

....

"I'm sorry, can you repeat that?" said Bushra.

....

4. Fill in the gaps in the passage below with direct speech and the right punctuation.

The forest was spooky after sunset. Ron was scared and turned to Freya.

....

Freya scowled at him. She didn't want to leave until they'd reached the cave.

....

They kept walking silently for an hour or so. Suddenly, a loud shriek came from the path ahead of them. Even Freya started to look uneasy now.

....

They both turned on their heels and ran all the way home.

An Extra Challenge

Mbali and Hana are planning a surprise party for their friend Theodore.
Can you write their conversation as direct speech?

Then see if you can continue their conversation so each person speaks three more times.

It's Theodore's birthday on Wednesday, Mbali. We need to plan something really special for him.

I agree Hana. Let's plan a surprise party with all of his friends and family.

"Can you tick a box to show how you did?" I asked politely.

13

Linking ideas

How It Works

Adverbials are groups of words that act like adverbs. Adverbials and adverbs tell you how, why, when, where or how often something happens. You can use them to link ideas together, which helps your writing flow smoothly. This is called 'cohesion'.

I'm going shopping this morning. Then, I'll meet up with Sally.

Adding an adverbial and an adverb to these sentences links the events together by telling you when they happened.

Ben loves swimming. He goes to the local pool most days.

This adverbial links the sentences by telling you how often something happens.

Now Try These

1. Circle the adverbial in each pair of sentences below.

   I love travelling. I am going to Italy next week.

   I couldn't find my rucksack. I looked for it under the chair.

   I am in the school play. Every evening, I practise my lines.

   I made gingerbread men. I ate them all very quickly.

2. Add a word or phrase from the box to each pair of sentences to link them together.

in two minutes	then	very gently	late at night

   She plays the drums .... The neighbours often complain.

   Harry ran to the door. He had to catch the bus ....

   First, fry the onions and garlic. .... , add the tomatoes.

   Hina stroked the rabbit .... She didn't want to scare it.

3. Rewrite the pairs of sentences below with an adverb or adverbial to link them together.

Horatio wrote a letter. He went to bed.

....

I live by the sea. I go to the beach.

....

4. Fill in each gap in this passage using a suitable adverb or adverbial.

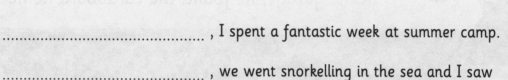

.... , I spent a fantastic week at summer camp.

.... , we went snorkelling in the sea and I saw

lots of fish. .... , we completed an obstacle course

in the forest. I was absolutely exhausted when we got back, so I went straight

to bed. .... , we cooked sausages on the campfire for

breakfast. .... , we did a treasure hunt for chocolate.

An Extra Challenge

This storyboard shows Flora's daily routine. Can you write a passage describing her routine? Make sure you use adverbs and adverbials to link your ideas together.

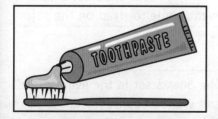

Are you a master of linking ideas? Give a box a tick.

Linking paragraphs

Adverbs and adverbials can be used to link paragraphs together smoothly.
They often link paragraphs by showing a change in time, place or number.

time   ⟶ Last week, Oscar decided to make a model castle.

number ⟶ Firstly, he drew a rough design on some paper.

place   ⟶ In the garage, he found the cardboard he needed.

Now Try These

1. Put each word or phrase into the correct box to show
   whether they could link paragraphs by time, place or number.

that afternoon   at the park   firstly   under the bridge

thirdly   lastly   nearby   tomorrow   on Tuesday

Time	Place	Number
....	....	....
....	....	....
....	....	....

2. Draw lines to match each blue box to the word or
   phrase that best links the paragraphs in that box.

Last year, I went on holiday to Madrid. It was really fun.
...... , I'm flying to Barcelona with my family and I can't wait.

In the kitchen

Before going to the gym, I stretched and drank some water.
...... , I was exhausted, so I went home to sleep on the sofa.

Secondly

Firstly, you need to weigh out all of your ingredients.
...... , put all your dry ingredients in a mixing bowl.

This summer

The guests sat in the living room and waited calmly for dinner.
...... , Mike was struggling to make all three courses himself.

Afterwards

3. Add a different adverbial to each paragraph to link them together smoothly.

...., Amancio's family set off to the rescue shelter. They were going to adopt a dog and Amancio was filled with joy.

...., Amancio heard the excitable dogs. Their sweet faces peeked through the bars, eager to greet them.

...., he spotted a face hidden by grey fur. As he approached the bars, so did the dog. The dog's tail started to wag.

4. Write the first sentence of the next paragraph in each story, starting with an adverbial.

a)   The valiant knight rode towards the tower in the distance. There was an eerie silence and she felt as if something was watching her. She didn't like it at all.

....

....

b)   According to the recipe, I already had the majority of the ingredients I needed to make my biscuits for the school fair. I just needed to buy some chocolate chips.

....

....

An Extra Challenge

Read what Sadie says about her day. Can you write three more paragraphs that start with adverbs or adverbials to continue Sadie's story?

Last weekend, I went shopping with my dad to buy presents for my grandma's birthday. She really likes bird-watching, so Dad wanted one of her gifts to be a new pair of binoculars. After trying a few shops, we managed to find the perfect pair.

At lunchtime, we went to a small café near the cathedral. It sold all sorts of sandwiches and fancy cakes — I wanted to try all of them! Dad ordered a cheese baguette with plenty of salad, and I asked for an egg and cress roll.

Are you in para-dise? Tick a box to show how you got on.

Classroom conundrum

Eleanor and her classmates are chatting about their ideas for their creative writing, but they're all talking over each other. Can you work out what the words are that Eleanor didn't quite hear? Once you think you've figured out what each pupil said, find the missing words in the wordsearch to check that you're correct.

I am going to use plenty of adverbs and __ __ j __ __ t __ __ __ s to make my story interesting.

Do you think "I'm running as fast as a stream" sounds like a good __ i __ i __ __ ?

Have I written this __ __ __ __ __ t __ __ __ clause correctly? "The shop that she lives above is a bakery."

Can you help me think of a snappy __ e a __ __ __ __ __ e for my newspaper article?

I'll use d __ __ e __ t __ p __ __ __ __ to write a conversation between the characters.

I'm going to create a l __ __ e __ __ like the story of Robin Hood.

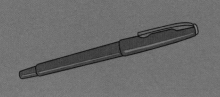

I need to remember to __ d __ __ __ my work at the end.

I've written "The stampede was an unstoppable wave." I think that's a good __ e __ __ __ p __ __ __ __ .

I'm writing a poem, so I need to decide on a r __ __ __ __ e scheme.

Why don't you use an adverbial to __ __ __ __ k your i __ __ __ __ __ s together?

```
K F M N I A Z F Z U H T F S G
X R K C D V W H C I I J V A M
P H P L E K I J E D A K D X M
R Y L R A D Z V E A H K E V B
J M E Z S X A O W P D G H U K
T E G S U L W F V A E L M A Y
Y R A E E O D M H N A I I G O
M A R G A Q C B Q R C N Y N R
H U E S I M I L E K V K V A E
I N M X O P G O U W F H C W L
D V H C E E P S T C E R I D A
N Q E J N I U Z I D L I H Z T
S Z D M G N X Q F D N K T Z I
O R F U A D J E C T I V E S V
R O H P A T E M P N Z W H A E
```

19

Similes

A simile is a way of describing something by comparing it to something else.

Damian zoomed through the playground like a train.

The football coach turned as purple as a beetroot.

Similes usually use the words 'like' or 'as'.

You can use similes in your writing to make it more interesting. Similes can also make it easier for the reader to imagine what you are describing.

Now Try These

1. Tick the box next to each sentence that contains a simile.

The powerful rocket rumbled loudly as it surged into the sky. ☐

"Get out!" shouted my brother, his voice booming like thunder. ☐

Toni thinks all sweets are delicious, but she doesn't like chocolate. ☐

My sister bought a new jumper that is as blue as the ocean. ☐

2. Draw lines to join these similes together.

Emir sped through the water like	old wooden floorboards.
Katherine whispered as quietly as	a sleek otter.
The biscuit crumbled in my hand like	dry sand.
The woman's knees were as creaky as	a mouse.

3. Finish these sentences using your own similes.

The elephant is as big as ....

The fan hummed like ....

She ran across the field like ....

Samira's voice is as loud as ....

The dog's fur is as black as ....

4. Rewrite each sentence, adding a simile to make it more interesting.

The race car sped away.

....

The skydiver glided down.

....

Tara held the baby.

....

An Extra Challenge

Take a look at this picture of cowboys in a desert.

Can you come up with four similes to describe the things you can see in this picture?

Do you feel as wise as an owl when it comes to similes?

21

Metaphors

How It Works

A metaphor is a way of describing something by saying it is something else.

The pepperoni pizza is a slice of heaven.

The clouds are a blanket covering the sky.

As with similes, you can use metaphors to make your writing more interesting and to help the reader imagine what you are describing.

Now Try These

1. Circle the boxes that contain a metaphor.

My dad puts out fires because he is a firefighter.	My sister sings like a screeching cat.	The old woman's fingers were crooked twigs.
On the rollercoaster, Polly's face turned as green as a frog.	The leaves are large snowflakes falling to the ground.	The greenhouse is a furnace in the summer.

2. Use the words below to complete the metaphors.

engine	sunshine	bees	pearl

The crowd was an angry swarm of ....

Monica's smile is a ray of .... on a cloudy day.

The purring cat on my lap is a rumbling ....

The cathedral is the .... of the city centre.

3. Rewrite each sentence so that it uses a different metaphor.

Her hair is a woolly sheep.

Her hair is ....

The fog was a gloomy curtain.

The fog was ....

4. Rewrite each sentence, adding a metaphor to make it more interesting.

The stars are shining brightly in the night sky.

....

....

The tornado was charging towards the barn.

....

....

Take a look at these pictures.
Can you write a sentence
that contains a metaphor to
describe each one?

Have you mastered your
metaphors? Tick a box.

23

Poems

How It Works

Poems often use rhymes and lots of description.

I chased a football on the pitch,
But then it fell into a ditch.
Out of the soil appeared a mole.
Who kicked the ball and shouted "Goal!"

Each pair of lines rhymes.

Similes and metaphors can help make your poems more interesting. You can also use personification — this is where you use human qualities to describe something that isn't human.

The light winked at me through the leaves.

This is personification — the light 'winked', which is a human action.

Now Try These

The Giant Barber

Once upon a time there lived a giant,
Who had a barber shop in his cave.
One day, he met a clumsy client,
Who went by the name of Dave.

Dave stumbled through the barber's door
His face covered by thick, knotty hair.
He tripped up and fell onto the floor,
And the barber helped him into a chair.

The barber whipped out his trusty shears,
And hundreds of hairs let out a groan.
He chopped and cut round Dave's ears
And a matted clump dropped like a stone.

Dave's face was no longer concealed.
"Amazing!" he exclaimed. "I can see!"
His surroundings now clearly revealed,
Dave thanked the barber and paid his fee.

1. What is the rhyme scheme of the poem? Circle one box.

ABBA   ABAB   AABB   ABAC

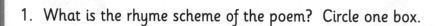

2. Find and copy a line from the poem that uses personification.

....

3. "And a matted clump dropped like a stone."
   What is this line an example of? Circle one box.

   | simile | metaphor | personification |

4. Why do you think Dave was clumsy when he entered the giant's barber shop?

....

....

5. Rewrite these sentences using personification.

   The scissors moved through the hair.

....

....

   The barber's chair creaked loudly.

....

An Extra Challenge

Can you write a poem about one of the characters below?
Choose one name, a rhyme scheme and an event to use in your poem.

NAMES	RHYME SCHEMES	EVENTS
Forgetful Faiza	AABB	rescuing a cat
Posh Paolo	ABAB	pranking a friend
Heroic Harry	AAAA	throwing a party
Wicked Wendy	ABBA	losing a tortoise
	ABAC	

Are your rhymes sublime?
Tick a box to show how you did.

Myths and legends

How It Works

Myths and legends are traditional stories that have been passed down the generations.

Myths are ancient stories which often try to explain the world around us.
Myths often involve gods, heroes and the supernatural. Some examples are:

Theseus and the Minotaur   Isis and Osiris   Fenrir the Wolf

Legends are believed to be based on real people and events, but the details
have often been changed or exaggerated over time. Some examples are:

Robin Hood   Saint George and the Dragon

Now Try These

Here is an extract from a Viking myth that explains how the world was created.

> A long time ago, the universe was a bleak place of ice and fire that was ruled by an evil giant named Ymir. Three gods, Odin, Vili and Ve, wanted to rid the universe of evil and create a better world, so they battled Ymir and defeated him. From Ymir's body they created a beautiful world of oceans, rivers and trees. Then, they tasked two gods named Sol and Mani to repeatedly pull chariots containing the sun and moon across the sky. After this, Odin transformed two trees into a man and a woman — they were the first humans. The gods named the human world Midgard and joined it with a rainbow bridge to Asgard, the world of the gods.

1. Circle the word that best describes the universe when Ymir ruled it.

    dull   peaceful   unpleasant   beautiful

2. How did Odin, Vili and Ve create day and night?

    ....

    ....

3. How can you tell that this extract is from a myth?

    ....

    ....

Here is an extract from the legend of King Arthur. We can't know for certain whether Arthur existed or not, but it is thought he may have ruled Britain around 1,500 years ago.

> After breaking his sword in battle, Arthur needed to find a new one worthy of a king. One day, the wizard Merlin took him to a large and serene lake. There, Arthur saw an arm rising out from beneath the water, holding aloft a magnificent sword. At that moment, a woman appeared, who was known as the Lady of the Lake. She told the king that he could have the sword in return for a favour she would ask for in the future. Arthur readily agreed and he and Merlin rowed out to retrieve the gleaming sword. Rowing back to the shore, Merlin gave Arthur an important piece of advice.
>
> "Make sure you cherish the sword's case as much as the sword itself, Arthur. As long as you keep the case with you, you shall never come to any harm."

4. a) Write down one way the story makes the sword seem magical.

    ....

    b) Give an example of something else magical in the story.

    ....

5. Do you think Arthur was right to accept the sword? Explain your answer.

    ....

    ....

An Extra Challenge

Can you turn the wolf in the text below into a legendary creature by changing or exaggerating details in the text? For example, you could try turning the wolf into a monster or giving it magical powers.

> Many hundreds of years ago, the village of Oakby was plagued by a wolf that crept into the village and stole chickens and sheep. It moved quietly in the dead of night, so few people ever saw it. One villager said she had seen its eyes glinting in the darkness. Another claimed that it had large teeth. A third had never seen the wolf itself, but insisted that he often found its paw prints outside his house.

Can you write a legend about your creature? Imagine that the villagers managed to stop it from attacking their village. How might they have managed to do this?

Do you feel legendary after finishing these pages?

Fact-finding

How It Works

When you're reading non-fiction texts, you need to be able to pick out facts.

There are lots of facts in this sentence:

Julius Caesar **was** a Roman ruler **who** fought many battles.

his name   who he was   what he did

Now Try These

Read this extract about the Romans invading Britain.

> In 55 BC, Julius Caesar attempted to invade Britain. He led an army of two Roman legions — around 10 000 men — on dozens of ships. Caesar had initially planned to land at Dover, but he found Celts (people who lived in Britain) waiting for him there. He decided to sail a short way northeast to seek a new landing zone. There, he was met with fierce resistance from the Celts who had tracked the fleet along the coast. The landing was chaotic but Caesar and his men managed to push the defenders back. However, the Romans made little progress against the Celts and storms damaged Caesar's ships. The Romans gave up and left Britain.
>
> A year later, Caesar returned to Britain with an army of around 25 000. Despite forcing some Celtic tribes to surrender to him, Caesar had to leave Britain yet again, this time to end a rebellion elsewhere. It wasn't until 43 AD that the Romans returned under the leadership of Emperor Claudius and Britain was finally brought under Roman rule.

1. Roughly how many soldiers did Caesar bring with him when he first invaded Britain?

   ....

2. Why didn't Caesar land at Dover during the first invasion?

   ....

3. Why did Caesar and his army leave Britain after the second invasion?

   ....

Read this extract about the impact the Romans had on Britain.

> The Romans faced a lot of resistance from tribes throughout Britain such as the Scots, Picts and Saxons. The Romans governed the country for nearly 400 years before they retreated in 410 AD.
>
> The Romans left a lasting legacy in Britain. They established many settlements, such as Londinium, which developed into the London we know today. Places in England that end in 'chester', 'cester' or 'caster' were all once Roman settlements. The Romans also constructed a network of roads to link their towns and forts, and some of these routes are still used today. For example, Watling Street was a major Roman road that ran across England between Dover and Wroxeter in Shropshire. Today, modern roads still follow much of this route.

4. Give two examples of how the effects of the Roman invasion are still felt today.

    ....

    ....

5. Read these statements about the two texts you've read, then decide whether each statement is true or false.

	True	False
Emperor Claudius brought Britain under Roman rule.	☐	☐
The Romans ruled Britain for almost six centuries.	☐	☐
There was once a Roman settlement at Lancaster.	☐	☐

An Extra Challenge

Here are some facts about a British queen called Boudica, who led a rebellion against the Romans. Can you write a paragraph that links all these facts together in a sensible order?

Boudica was the queen of the Iceni tribe.	Boudica's army burned down the cities of Colchester and London.	The cities were poorly defended because many Roman soldiers were in Wales.

Boudica formed an army and led a rebellion against the Romans.

The Romans tried to seize Iceni land when Boudica's husband died.	The Iceni lived in south east England.

The Roman soldiers returned from Wales and defeated Boudica's army.

Are you the best fact-finder in history? Tick a box.

Newspaper articles

How It Works

Newspaper articles use the past tense to tell you about an event that has already happened.

Articles often use a snappy headline to get your attention. Headlines can use techniques such as a play on words. Take a look at this example:

TEA-DRINKING CONTESTANT IN HOT WATER

"In hot water" means to be in trouble but it also relates to drinking tea.

Articles can give facts and opinions.

She was caught cheating. ← This is a fact — it gives information that can be proved.

"It's a dark day for tea drinkers around the world." ← This is an opinion — it's what someone believes but it can't be proved. Articles often use direct speech to show people's opinions.

Now Try These

Read this newspaper article.

BAD WEATHER STORMS INTO SCOTLAND

Large parts of Scotland were buffeted by freak winds and heavy rain last weekend. The storm, named Storm Cedric, caused disruption and damage in many areas.

The persistent torrential rain on Saturday and Sunday brought with it rapidly rising water levels. As a result, there was a rush to send out sandbags to prevent the floodwater entering people's homes.

Douglas Sinclair from Fife described the scene that unfolded on Saturday: "It was madness — I haven't seen a storm like that in ages. The rain poured down so heavily!

 There were trees on the ground and the wind didn't show any signs of stopping. The whole thing was pretty terrifying."

The storm caused chaos on the roads too. Motorways were flooded, which brought traffic to a standstill. Bridges, such as the Forth Road Bridge, were temporarily closed due to the danger posed by the winds.

However, truck driver Maureen Davies said: "There was no need to close the bridge. It was only a bit of wind! I've seen worse storms — people are overreacting."

1. How is the title of the article a play on words?

....

....

2. Tick the correct box in the table below to show whether each statement is a fact or an opinion.

	Fact	Opinion
People used sandbags to protect their homes.		
The storm was a scary experience.		
The storm affected motorways and bridges.		

3. A journalist has mistakenly used the present tense to write the sentences below. Rewrite them in the past tense.

> During the storm, thousands of homes are left without power.
> Evacuations take place as the water threatens to enter people's houses.

....

....

....

4. Do you think Douglas Sinclair and Maureen Davies felt the same way about the storm? How can you tell?

....

....

....

An Extra Challenge

Can you write a newspaper article about a famous person visiting your school? Make sure you write a headline, use columns and include direct speech to show people's opinions of the event. Here are some things you could include in your article:

Who is the celebrity?   **Where did they visit?**

Why did they visit?   **When did they visit?**

What happened?   **How did people feel?**

Did you storm through these pages? Tick a box.

Points of view

How It Works

Different people can see the same event differently. This is called their point of view. The examples below show the points of view of three different people.

I hid behind the door and made Sarah jump. It was so funny.

I was really scared when Steve jumped out from behind the door.

I saw Steve make Sarah jump. I thought it was childish.

These examples are all written in the first person.
The first person uses words like 'I', 'me' and 'my'.

Now Try These

1. Read the short story below, then match each character to the sentence which describes their point of view.

The finish line was in sight and Tom, Hannah and Yasmin were neck and neck. However, Hannah soon found she couldn't keep up with the pace and fell back. Then, Tom started limping and had to stop. Yasmin believed the medal was definitely hers, but suddenly Henry came from nowhere and beat her to the finish line.

Tom

Hannah

Yasmin

Henry

"I thought no one could beat me now."

"My foot really hurt."

"I was determined to catch up and win."

"I was just too tired."

2. Read the sentence below about Matt and Kyra. Then, write two sentences in the first person to follow it, one from Matt's point of view and one from Kyra's.

Matt felt exhausted during the hike, but Kyra seemed full of energy.

Matt ➡ ....

Kyra ➡ ....

3. Read these two descriptions of the same event. How does the waiter's
    point of view change the reader's opinion of the customer?

CUSTOMER	WAITER
I went to a restaurant yesterday evening and the service was terrible. The waiter had no clue about the menu and couldn't answer any of my simple questions. I politely but firmly asked if he could get someone more senior for me to talk to.	It was only my second shift at the restaurant, but I had studied the menu in detail. Unfortunately, I served a woman who asked bizarre questions that were impossible to answer. She was also impatient and rude, and she demanded to speak to someone more senior.

....

....

....

4. Rewrite these sentences so they are from Hasan's point of view. Use the first person.

    James laughed as he watched Hasan being chased around the playground
    by a bee. However, he suddenly felt rather guilty when it stung Hasan.

....

....

....

An Extra Challenge

Read this short story about Rosa and Nate. Can you rewrite the story from
Nate's point of view, using the first person? Think about how Nate might
be feeling and how he might act at different points in the story.

Rosa and her brother Nate were about to make their first plane
journey. While Rosa was excited to experience her first take-off,
Nate felt very nervous. The engines roared and began to propel
the aircraft down the runway. It was at this point that Rosa looked
at Nate and saw how frightened he was. She held his hand and
smiled at him, which seemed to calm him down. The jet lurched
off the ground and into the sky — the holiday had begun.

What's your point of view on
these pages? Give a box a tick.

Editing your work

How It Works

When you finish a piece of writing, you need to check it carefully.

- Check that you've used the same tense throughout your work.

- Add or replace words to make your writing more interesting.

  The bird flapped ~~hard~~ frantically to escape the vicious cat.

  'Frantically' is more imaginative than 'hard'.   Adding 'vicious' makes the sentence more interesting.

- Remove any unnecessary words that are repetitive or don't add anything to the text.

  I don't like ~~boring~~ romance films because I think they're boring.

Now Try These

1. The diary extract below is describing a football match. Underline the words that are in the wrong tense, and write the correct word above them.

    Last night's football match was a real nail-biter. There is one minute left

    on the clock and the score was 1-1. Ullsford Town's star player passes the

    ball to Joan, who has a chance to kick it into the goal. Joan launched the ball

    across the field and it flies straight into the net. Half the stadium cheers wildly.

    Joan's teammates run over and lifted her triumphantly onto their shoulders.

2. Read the passage below and cross out any words that don't add any new information.

    On Saturday, we had a really fun and great trip to the zoo at
    the weekend. When we arrived at the zoo, we went straight
    to see the penguins as soon as we got there. I was thrilled
    when the zookeeper let me feed the penguins with food, and
    I was very excited. Then it started raining, so we went inside
    a café to have lunch inside. Afterwards, we went to see the
    giraffes in the giraffe enclosure. They were quite shy.

3. Make these sentences more interesting by adding a word on each dotted line.

The king wore his .... crown.

George spoke .... to the small puppy.

The rock band performed to the .... crowd.

Zofia drove .... down the narrow lane.

4. Rewrite each sentence below, replacing the underlined word with a more imaginative one. Be careful not to change the meaning of the sentences.

We were <u>happy</u> that Ava could come to the party.

....

Sadiq is off today because he has a <u>bad</u> cough.

....

My mum <u>shouted</u>, "There's a spider in the bath!"

....

An Extra Challenge

Samantha has written a paragraph about her trip to a theme park. Can you edit what she has written to improve it? Think about tweaking the paragraph so that it uses the same tense throughout, adding in more interesting words and removing unnecessary ones.

> We went to a theme park yesterday — I had never been to a theme park before so I was excited! When we arrive, my parents show me and my brother a map of the theme park. It was big and there were lots of good rides. I wanted to go straight to the biggest ride first, but when we got to the biggest ride, I change my mind. Gazing up at the ride, I suddenly felt scared so my dad takes me to a smaller ride. We get into a cart and the carts soon started to move along the tracks up a slope. I liked it when we went down the other side.

Did these pages go ~~well~~ brilliantly? Tick a box.

Answers

Pages 2-3 — Word types

1. Bosede and Ian <u>walk</u> to the beach. — e.g. run
   Marius <u>made</u> a cake for his birthday. — e.g. baked
   I <u>saw</u> an eagle on my way to school. — e.g. spotted
   She <u>likes</u> her mother's dresses. — e.g. adores

2. Briony <u>sings</u> sweetly to her son. — verb
   My dad is too <u>competitive</u> at board games. — adjective
   It was unusually <u>busy</u> at the park today. — adjective
   The girl <u>ran</u> speedily down the road. — verb

3. Any sensible answers, e.g.
   Rasheed <u>drove</u> to the supermarket. — verb
   I decided to wear my <u>favourite</u> jumper. — adjective
   Her cat <u>constantly</u> scratches the furniture. — adverb
   Delilah poured the soup into a <u>bowl</u>. — noun

4. Any sensible sentences, e.g. The elegant swan moved gracefully across the lake. / Lola is always telling hilarious tales. / The thief crept silently towards the shiny necklace.

   An Extra Challenge

   Any sensible adjectives and adverbs added to the story.

Pages 4-5 — Degrees of possibility

1. Helen <u>possibly</u> won't have time to wash the dishes. — 3
   I will <u>definitely</u> have a slice of that huge chocolate cake. — 1
   Bill and Ted will <u>probably</u> go to the theme park with me. — 2

2. Any sensible adverbs, e.g. Dmitry is <u>possibly</u> going to go fishing tomorrow. / <u>Perhaps</u> I'll order a strawberry milkshake. / I think that Megan will <u>probably</u> win the race today. / <u>Maybe</u> he won't find the hidden message.

3. You should have circled: will, must, shall, must.

4. Any sensible sentences, e.g. I could go to Sasha's house this afternoon. / You might need to book a table at the restaurant. / I will try my best to finish my homework.
   You should have ticked the sentence that uses 'will'.

   An Extra Challenge

   Any sensible sentences, e.g. Lucy will probably win the tennis match. / Daniel may catch the butterfly. / Kieran might score a goal. / Sid must not let the ball go into the net. / Marta is certainly going to eat all the jam.
   You should have coloured these sentences blue:
   Sid must... / Marta is certainly...
   You should have coloured these sentences red:
   Lucy will probably... / Daniel may... / Kieran might...

Pages 6-7 — Relative clauses

1. I can't wait to go back to the café — where we had the best apple pie.
   Gary loved hiking in the mountains — that were always covered in snow.
   My new neighbour is Dr Petrov — who is a famous scientist.
   Farah needs a dress for the party — which starts at eight o'clock.

2. There is the man I saw looking for his keys earlier.
   The soup Rachel was preparing smelt delicious.

3. The scarf <u>that my nan knitted me</u> is very warm. — that
   Max, <u>whose car had broken down</u>, asked me for help. — whose
   Are there any lakes nearby <u>which we can swim in</u>? — which
   The hotel <u>that is around the corner</u> has a new chef. — that
   She is visiting her friend <u>who lives in Australia</u>. — who

4. Any sensible relative clauses, e.g.
   I am reading the book that Fiona recommended.
   The cinema where my dad works is closed today.
   Kara helped the boy who had grazed his knee.
   Lesley, whose alarm clock is broken, was late for school.

   An Extra Challenge

   Any sensible sentences that contain a relative clause, e.g. The owl that is sitting on that branch has just winked at me. / Ebele, who loves to draw, is sketching her garden. / I saw a ghost who was holding a black flag. / The dog that lives down the road is chasing the rabbit. / There is a wheelbarrow over there which is full of flowers. / Sam is washing the car that his aunty has just bought.

Pages 8-9 — Homophones

1. You should have ticked:
   The bride walked gracefully down the <u>isle</u>. — aisle
   The stormy sky was the colour of <u>steal</u>. — steel
   I think that roses are a <u>cymbal</u> of love. — symbol

2. alter, past, compliment, draught, who's

3. I do <u>not</u> think that you should tie that <u>knot</u> there.
   You need to <u>hire</u> a guide to climb <u>higher</u> up.
   Janice <u>guessed</u> that their <u>guest</u> would be late.
   You should take the <u>route</u> that passes the broken tree <u>root</u>.
   The <u>sight</u> of the ancient burial <u>site</u> was impressive.

4. Any sensible sentences, e.g. I like peace and quiet when I study. / I would like a piece of pie. / The current headteacher is retiring. / My nan doesn't like currant buns.

   An Extra Challenge

   The narrow part of your body above your hips — waist / Not moving — stationary / A period of seven days — week / A group of musicians — band / Materials you use for writing — stationery / Cause something to split into pieces — break / Prevented from doing something by law — banned / Another word for the noun 'rubbish' — waste / Lacking strength or energy — weak / Something you do to slow down a bike or car — brake

   Any sensible paragraph that includes at least one word from each pair of homophones.

Pages 10-11 — Tricky words

1. var<u>ie</u>ty, c<u>ei</u>ling, rec<u>ei</u>ved, prot<u>ei</u>n, fr<u>ie</u>ndly

2. dough — though / enough — tough / sought — fought / cough — trough

3. bowed, through, rough, thoughtful

4. Silvia loves to <u>nit</u> scarves for all her relatives. — knit
   <u>Gosts</u> wander the halls of the old mansion. — Ghosts
   The students <u>lisened</u> to the teacher attentively. — listened
   Nathan has taken a <u>rong</u> turn in his car. — wrong

5. Any sensible sentences, e.g. I waved to my new <u>neighbour</u>. / We <u>brought</u> sandwiches to the park. / She picked some <u>raspberries</u> from her garden.

   An Extra Challenge

   autum<u>n</u> / sc<u>e</u>ne / hon<u>e</u>stly / g<u>u</u>ilty / plum<u>b</u>er / i<u>s</u>land / mus<u>c</u>les / clim<u>b</u>ed / <u>k</u>nocked / ans<u>w</u>ered / bris<u>t</u>led / W<u>h</u>ile / dou<u>b</u>t

Pages 12-13 — Direct speech

1. Zoey asked, "Are you there?"

Answers

Frank shouted, "Stop that!"
He said, "There's the pizza."

2. Any sensible answers to the questions, e.g. "I played tennis with my sister," replied Veronica. / "I was jumping on the sofa," said Kwame.

3. "Thank you," said Joe, "that is very kind of you."
"I'm sorry," said Bushra, "can you repeat that?"

4. Any sensible sentences, e.g. "I think we should head back," muttered Ron. / "But we're almost there!" complained Freya. / Freya whispered, "Maybe you were right, Ron. Let's go."

An Extra Challenge

"It's Theodore's birthday on Wednesday, Mbali," said Hana. "We need to plan something special for him."
Mbali replied, "I agree Hana. Let's plan a surprise party with all of his friends and family."

Any sensible extension of the conversation that uses direct speech and is punctuated correctly.

Pages 14-15 — Linking ideas

1. You should have underlined: next week / under the chair / Every evening / very quickly

2. She plays the drums <u>late at night</u>. The neighbours often complain. / Harry ran to the door. He had to catch the bus <u>in two minutes</u>. / First, fry the onions and garlic. <u>Then</u>, add the tomatoes. / Hina stroked the rabbit <u>very gently</u>. She didn't want to scare it.

3. Any sensible answers, e.g Horatio wrote a letter. Then he went to bed. / I live by the sea. I go to the beach every day.

4. <u>Last year</u>, I spent a fantastic week at summer camp. <u>On the first day</u>, we went snorkelling in the sea and I saw lots of fish. <u>In the afternoon</u>, we completed an obstacle course in the forest. I was absolutely exhausted when we got back, so I went straight to bed. <u>The next morning</u>, we cooked sausages on the campfire for breakfast. <u>After that</u>, we did a treasure hunt for chocolate.

An Extra Challenge

Any sensible passage that includes adverbs and adverbials, e.g. Every morning, Flora wakes up at half past seven. She gets dressed very quickly. Then, she makes breakfast. She brushes her teeth after she's eaten. She packs her bag in the hallway. Finally, she leaves the house to catch the bus.

Pages 16-17 — Linking paragraphs

1. Time — that afternoon / tomorrow / on Tuesday.
Place — at the park / under the bridge / nearby.
Number — firstly / thirdly / lastly.

2. In the kitchen — Mike was struggling to make all three courses himself. / Secondly — put all your dry ingredients in a mixing bowl. / This summer — I'm flying to Barcelona with my family and I can't wait. / Afterwards — I was exhausted, so I went home to sleep on the sofa.

3. Any sensible adverbials, e.g. In the morning / At the shelter / In the third cage

4. a) Any sensible sentence that starts with an adverbial, e.g. All of a sudden, she heard a thunderous roar burst through the clouds.
   b) Any sensible sentence that starts with an adverbial, e.g. At the supermarket, I couldn't find any chocolate chips so I had to buy raisins instead.

An Extra Challenge

Any sensible three paragraphs that start with adverbs or adverbials.

Pages 18-19 — Classroom conundrum

adjectives, simile, relative, headline, direct speech, legend, metaphor, rhyme, link, ideas, edit

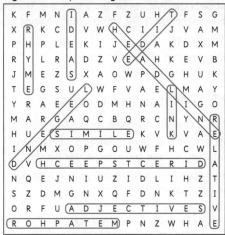

Pages 20-21 — Similes

1. "Get out!" shouted my brother, his voice booming like thunder. My sister bought a new jumper that is as blue as the ocean.

2. Emir sped through the water like — a sleek otter. / Katherine whispered as quietly as — a mouse. / The biscuit crumbled in my hand like — dry sand. / The woman's knees were as creaky as — old wooden floorboards.

3. Any sensible similes, e.g. The elephant is as big as <u>a truck</u>. / The fan hummed like <u>a wasps' nest</u>. / She ran across the field like <u>a cheetah</u>. / Samira's voice is as loud as <u>a lion's roar</u>. / The dog's fur is as black as <u>the night sky</u>.

4. Any sensible similes, e.g.
The race car sped away <u>like a bullet</u>.
The skydiver glided down <u>like a feather</u>.
Tara held the baby <u>like a precious jewel</u>.

An Extra Challenge

Any sensible similes, e.g. The horse galloped across the desert as fast as a hurricane.

Pages 22-23 — Metaphors

1. You should have circled: The old woman's fingers were crooked twigs. / The leaves are large snowflakes falling to the ground. / The greenhouse is a furnace in the summer.

2. The crowd was an angry swarm of <u>bees</u>.
Monica's smile is a ray of <u>sunshine</u> on a cloudy day.
The purring cat on my lap is a rumbling <u>engine</u>.
The cathedral is the <u>pearl</u> of the city centre.

3. Any sensible metaphors, e.g. Her hair is a large grey cloud. / The fog was a thick, solid wall.

4. Any sensible metaphors, e.g. The stars are tiny light bulbs, shining brightly in the night sky. / The tornado was an angry bull, charging towards the barn.

An Extra Challenge

Any sensible metaphors, e.g. The river is a snake slithering through the countryside.

Answers

Pages 24-25 — Poems

1. You should have circled: ABAB.

2. And hundreds of hairs let out a groan.

3. You should have circled: simile.

4. Any sensible answer, e.g. His hair was covering his eyes, so he couldn't see properly.

5. Any sensible sentences that use personification, e.g. The scissors chomped through the hair. / The barber's chair groaned loudly.

   An Extra Challenge

   Any sensible poem that uses one of the names, rhyme schemes and events.

Pages 26-27 — Myths and legends

1. You should have circled: unpleasant.

2. Any sensible answer, e.g. They tasked two gods to pull chariots containing the sun and moon across the sky.

3. Any sensible answer, e.g. It tells a story about gods and explains the world around us.

4. Any sensible answers, e.g.
   a) A mysterious arm holds it out of the lake.
   b) There is a wizard in the story.

5. Any sensible answer, e.g. Yes, because it meant he would have a sword to protect him. OR e.g. No, because the lady might ask Arthur for a favour he doesn't want to give.

   An Extra Challenge

   Any sensible changes to the text to turn the wolf into a legendary creature, e.g. You could have said that the wolf had flames for eyes and pawprints the size of dinner plates.

   Any sensible legend about the creature.

Pages 28-29 — Fact-finding

1. Around 10 000

2. There were Celtic warriors waiting for him.

3. They had to stop a rebellion elsewhere.

4. Any sensible answer, e.g. They founded London and built roads that we still follow the route of today.

5. Emperor Claudius brought Britain under Roman rule. — True
   The Romans ruled Britain for almost six centuries. — False
   There was once a Roman settlement at Lancaster. — True

   An Extra Challenge

   Any sensible paragraph, e.g. Boudica was the queen of the Iceni tribe. This tribe lived in south east England. The Romans tried to seize Iceni land when Boudica's husband died. However, Boudica formed an army and led a rebellion against the Romans. Her army burned down the cities of Colchester and London. These cities were poorly defended because many Roman soldiers were in Wales. In the end though, the Roman soldiers returned from Wales and defeated Boudica's army.

Pages 30-31 — Newspaper articles

1. Any sensible answer, e.g. The article is about a storm in Scotland but the headline also uses 'storms' as a verb to describe how the weather came to Scotland.

2. People used sandbags to protect their homes. — Fact
   The storm was a scary experience. — Opinion
   The storm affected motorways and bridges. — Fact

3. Any sensible answer that uses the past tense, e.g. During the storm, thousands of homes <u>were</u> left without power. Evacuations <u>took</u> place as the water <u>threatened</u> to enter people's houses.

4. Any sensible answer, e.g. No. Douglas thought the storm was bad and he was scared by it. Maureen didn't think the storm was that bad and believed people were just making a fuss.

   An Extra Challenge

   Any sensible article about a celebrity visiting your school that includes a headline, columns and direct speech.

Pages 32-33 — Points of view

1. Tom — "My foot really hurt." / Hannah — "I was just too tired." / Yasmin — "I thought no one could beat me now." / Henry — "I was determined to catch up and win."

2. Any sensible answers e.g.
   My legs ached trying to keep up with Kyra.
   I felt like I could run to the top of the mountain.

3. Any sensible answer, e.g. The customer's point of view made me think that the customer behaved in a reasonable way, but the waiter's point of view makes me think that the customer was actually unreasonable and rude.

4. Any sensible answer, e.g. The bee wouldn't stop chasing me. All James did was laugh, which was annoying. Then the bee stung me and it really hurt.

   An Extra Challenge

   Any sensible rewrite of the story from Nate's point of view, using the first person.

Pages 34-35 — Editing your work

1. Last night's football match was a real nail-biter. There <u>was</u> one minute left on the clock and the score was 1-1. Ullsford Town's star player <u>passed</u> the ball to Joan, who <u>had</u> a chance to kick it into the goal. Joan launched the ball across the field and it <u>flew</u> straight into the net. Half the stadium <u>cheered</u> wildly. Joan's teammates <u>ran</u> over and lifted her triumphantly onto their shoulders.

2. On Saturday, we had a really fun ~~and great~~ trip to the zoo ~~at the weekend~~. When we arrived ~~at the zoo~~, we went straight to see the penguins ~~as soon as we got there~~. I was thrilled when the zookeeper let me feed the penguins ~~with food, and I was very excited~~. Then it started raining, so we went inside a café to have lunch ~~inside~~. Afterwards, we went to see the giraffes ~~in the giraffe enclosure~~. They were quite shy.

3. Any sensible answers, e.g.
   The king wore his <u>magnificent</u> crown.
   George spoke <u>softly</u> to the small puppy.
   The rock band performed to the <u>excited</u> crowd.
   Zofia drove <u>cautiously</u> down the narrow lane.

4. Any sensible answers, e.g.
   We were <u>overjoyed</u> that Ava could come to the party.
   Sadiq is off today because he has a <u>dreadful</u> cough.
   My mum <u>screeched</u>, "There's a spider in the bath!"

   An Extra Challenge

   Any sensible changes to the paragraph, e.g. We went to a theme park yesterday — I had never been to one before so I was excited! When we arrived, my parents showed me and my brother a detailed map of the theme park.

EPF5Q21